But it's my turn to leave you . . .

Mel Calman

But it's my turn
to leave you...

Mandarin

BUT IT'S MY TURN TO LEAVE YOU . . .

First published in 1980 by Eyre Methuen Ltd

This edition published in 1991 by Mandarin Paperbacks
an imprint of Reed Consumer Books Limited
Michelin House, 81 Fulham Road, London SW3 6RB
and Auckland, Melbourne, Singapore and Toronto

Reprinted 1993

Copyright © 1980 Mel Calman

Designed by Philip Thompson

ISBN: 0 7493 0823 0

A CIP catalogue record for this book
is available from the British Library

Printed in England by Clays Ltd, St Ives plc

To my ex-wives . . . for their help with the research . . .

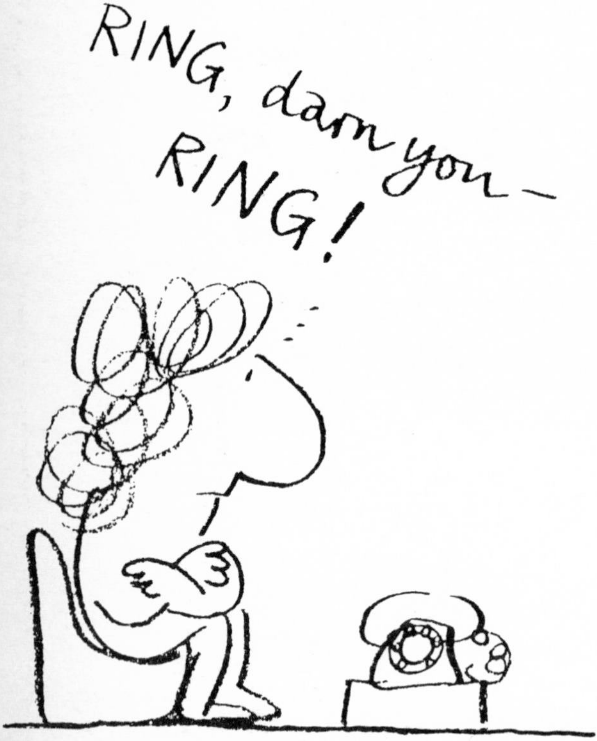
RING, darn you-
RING!

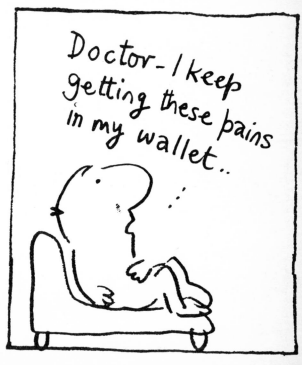

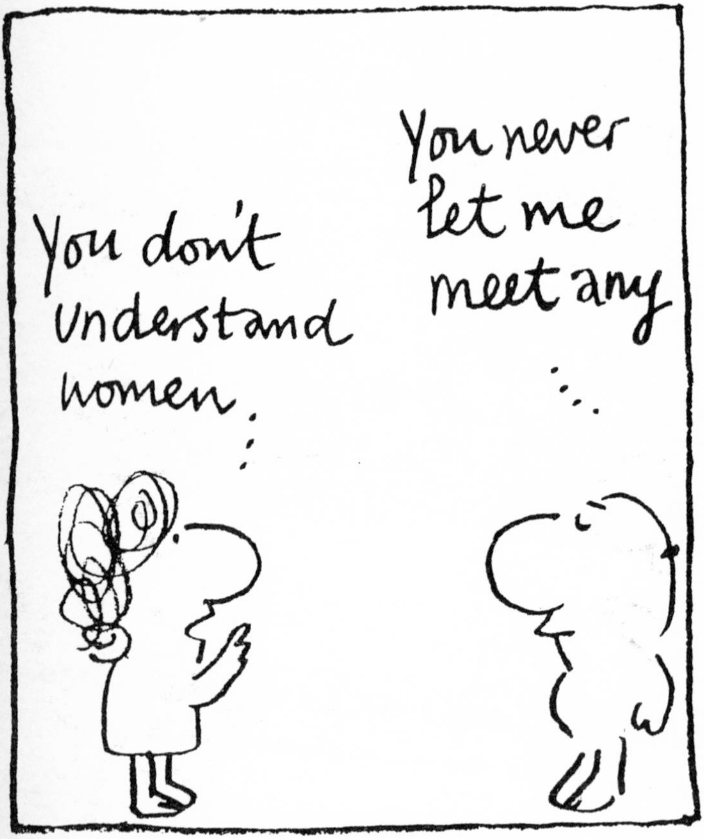
You don't understand women
You never let me meet any

Why aren't
you tender?

Because
I'm too
sore...

And don't talk to me until you're ready to listen!

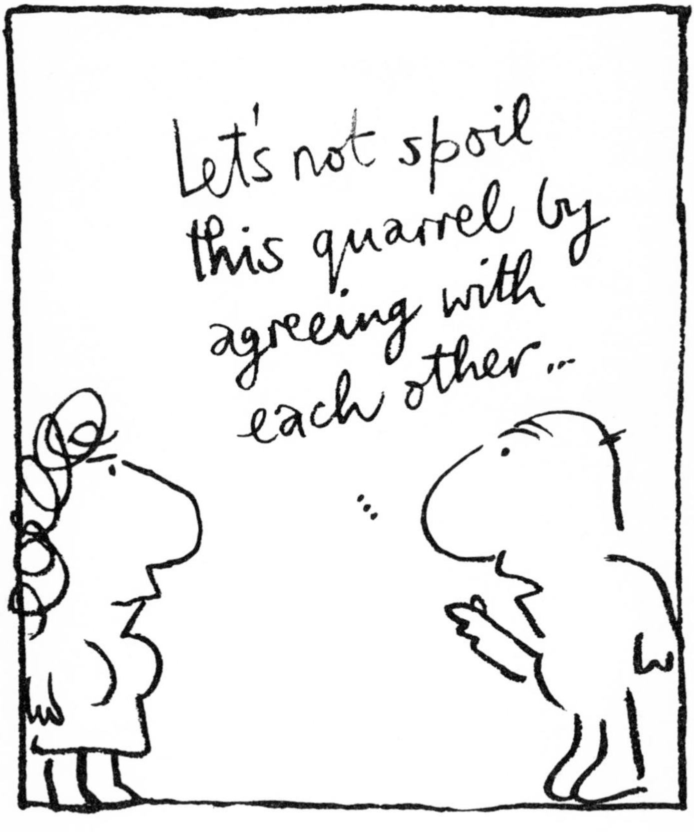
Let's not spoil this quarrel by agreeing with each other...

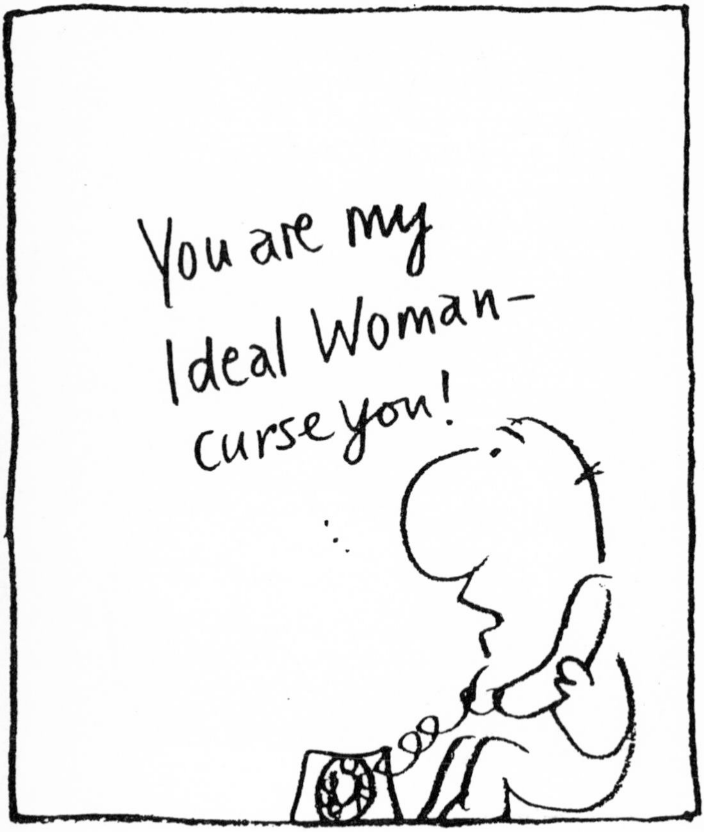
You are my Ideal Woman- curse you!

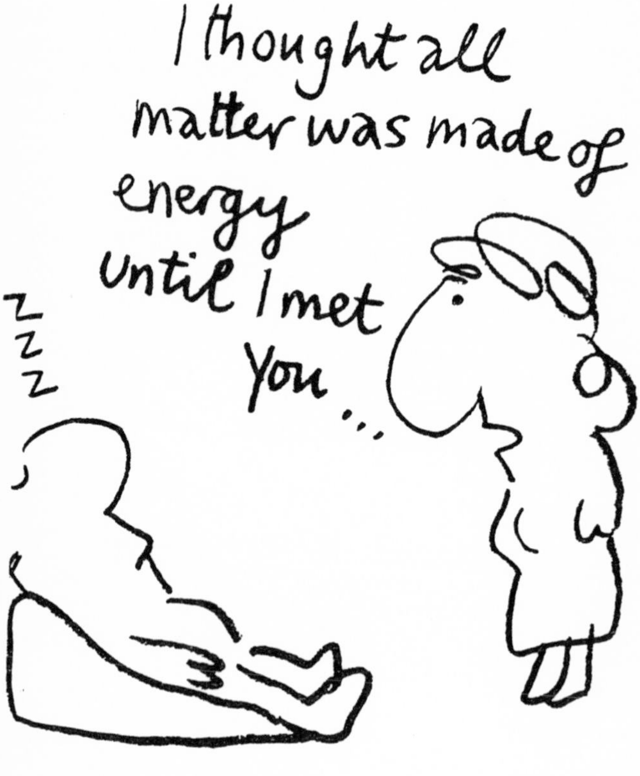

I thought all matter was made of energy until I met you...
ZZZ

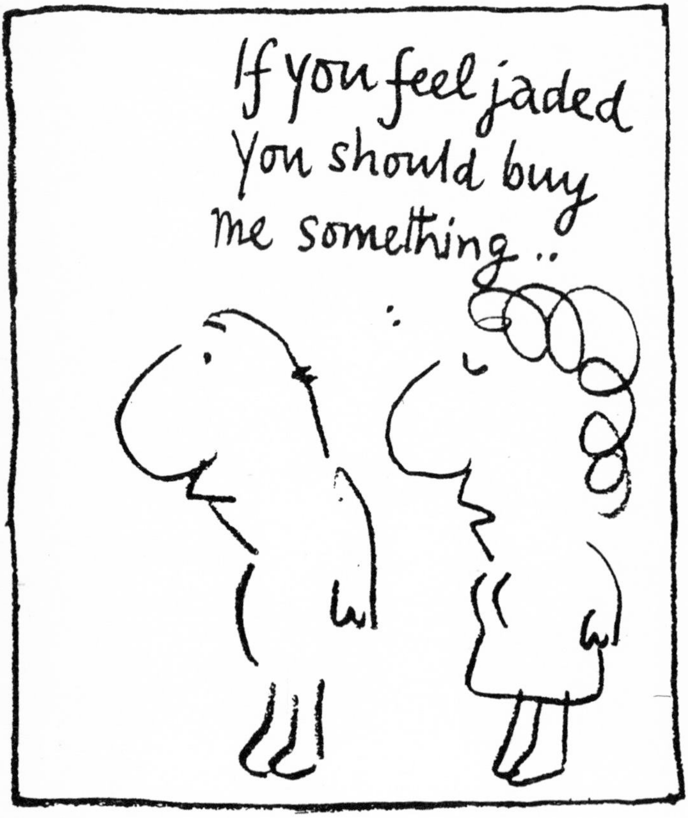
If you feel jaded
you should buy
me something..

I suppose a shallow person might find it profound...

Noël Coward told me he hated people who name-dropped..

That's just a female attitude..

Here's to Temperance..
I remember you - You came up, to me at last years party and asked me if I remembered you..
Step outside and say that!
Now tell me all about yourself - briefly...

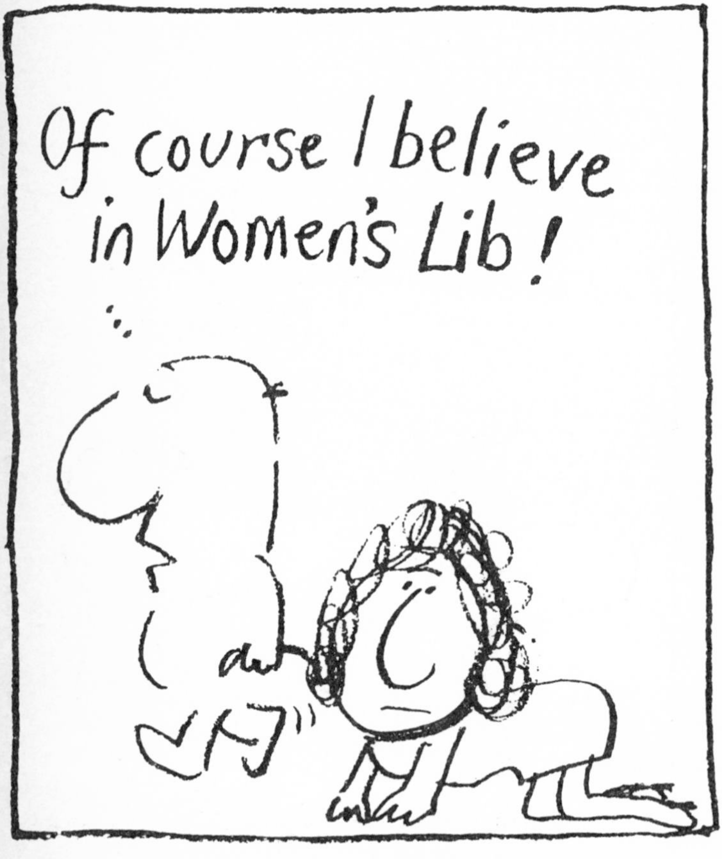
Of course I believe
in Women's Lib!

Look at it
from my
point of
view..

You're too
far away

it's your turn
to put the
quarrel out..

Something's missing from this romantic dinner...

Some awful man pressed his knee against mine all evening ...
That was me ..

I need this space between us - so as to be close to you ...

I tried an Encounter
Group – but
I didn't meet anyone...

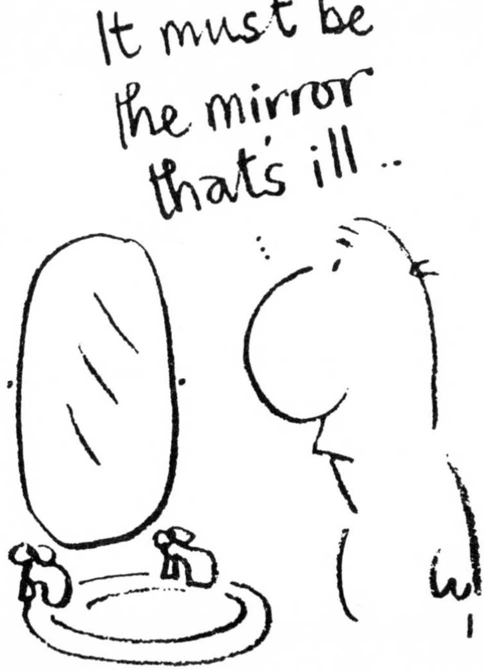
It must be
the mirror
that's ill..

Jogging is like
marriage - tiring
but good for you...

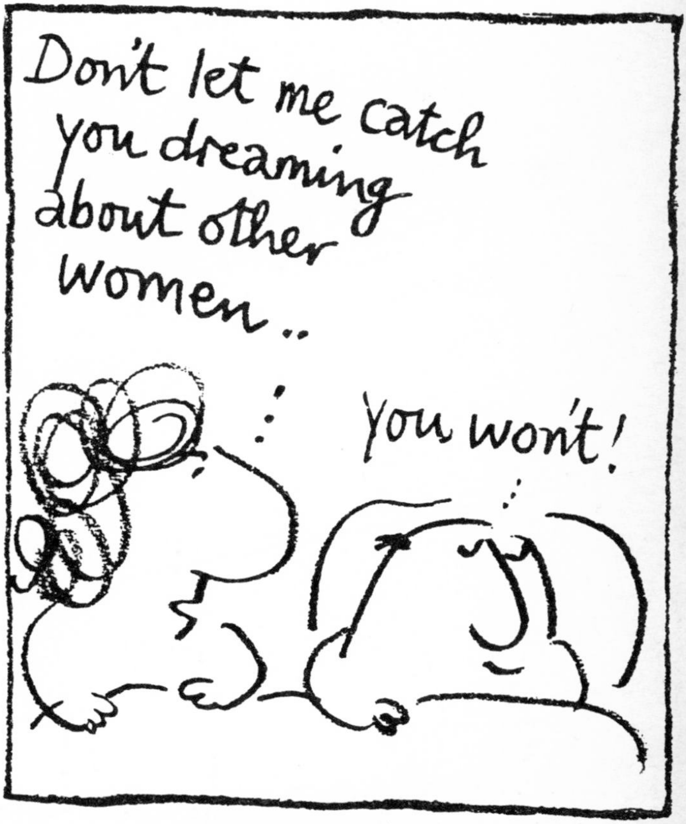
Don't let me catch you dreaming about other women..
You won't!

I've been more thrown against
than throwing..

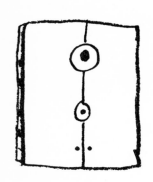

I understand it
and I still don't
like it

What
kind of
nonsense
is this?

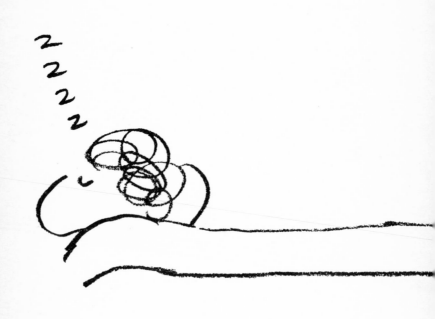

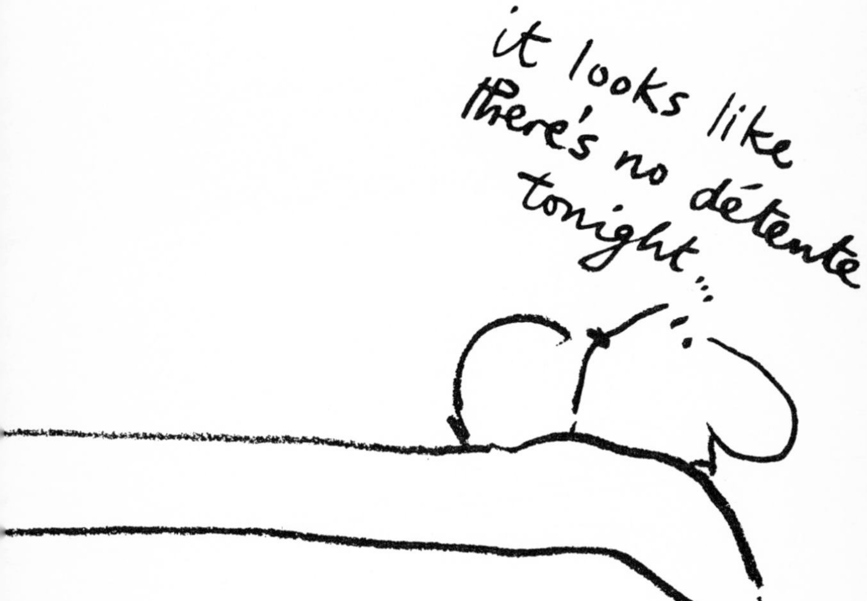
it looks like there's no détente tonight...

At least she still
sends me
her bills...

You can't put me on a pedestal and then expect me ... to dust it ..

She hasn't
seen my point
of view lately..

You're the kind of man
who takes his
clothes off and is
wearing another
suit underneath

How can
I have the last word —
if she doesn't
phone me?